BARGAIN WITH A STRANGER

Barbara Mitchelhill

Published in association with
The Basic Skills Agency

Hodder & Stoughton

A MEMBER OF THE HODDER

Acknowledgements
Cover: Lee Stinton/The Organisation.
Illustrations: Maureen Carter.

Orders: please contact Bookpoint Ltd, 130 Milton Park, Abingdon, Oxon OX14
4SB. Telephone: (44) 01235 827720, Fax: (44) 01235 400454. Lines are open
from 9.00–6.00, Monday to Saturday, with a 24 hour message answering
service. Email address: orders@bookpoint.co.uk

British Library Cataloguing in Publication Data
A catalogue record for this title is available from The British Library

ISBN 0 340 74775 7

First published 1999
Impression number   10 9 8 7 6 5 4 3 2
Year   2004 2003 2002

Typeset by Fakenham Photosetting Ltd, Fakenham, Norfolk
Printed in Great Britain for Hodder & Stoughton Educational, a division of
Hodder Headline Plc, 338 Euston Road, London NW1 3BH by Athenaeum
Press, Gateshead, Tyne & Wear.

Contents

1 The Poster

Daniel's downfall started
when they saw the poster.
His mates said,
'We can all sing.
Let's go for it!'

2 Fed up

Daniel wanted to be rich
and famous.
But he couldn't sing.
There was no way
he could be in a band.

3 If Only ...

He felt fed up
as he walked home.
He was broke.
If only he could sing,
he could be rich.

4 A Tall Dark Man

Suddenly, he felt a hand
on his arm.
He turned and saw
a tall dark man.
Daniel felt really scared.

5 Omar

The man's name was Omar.
'I can make you sing,' he said.
'How?' asked Daniel.

6 The Bargain

Omar didn't tell him.
'Just give me the money
from the first tour,' he said.
Daniel agreed.
It would be worth it.

7 Daniel Gets the Job

All the kids went to the club.
Daniel's voice was brilliant.
'You get the job, Daniel,'
said the manager.

8 Getting Started

The first tour started
the next week.
As the coach pulled away,
Daniel saw Omar
watching in the crowd.

9 The First Gig

The first gig
was a great success.
The crowd went wild.
Daniel knew he was going
to be rich and famous.

10 The Note

After the gig,
Daniel went to his room.
Someone had pushed a note
under the door.
It was Omar.

11 Daniel Won't Pay

Daniel locked the door.
He wasn't going to give Omar
the money.
He was going to be
really rich.

12 Omar Follows

In every town, Omar followed.
He was like a long
black shadow.
But Daniel wouldn't
speak to him.

13 To the USA

When the British tour
was finished,
the next one was in the States.
Omar wouldn't follow him there.

14 In the Crowd

'He'll never find me,'
thought Daniel.
But he was wrong.
In New York,
he saw Omar
in the crowd.

15 Night Fright

In the middle of the night,
Daniel woke up shaking.
Someone was standing over him.
It was Omar.

16 Omar's Demand

'Now keep your part
of the bargain,' Omar said.
'No,' said Daniel.
'You can't have the money!'
Slowly Omar turned away
and walked to the door.

17 Get on with it!

The next night
Daniel went on stage.
He opened his mouth to sing –
but nothing came out.
The crowd shouted,
'GET ON WITH IT!'

18 Omar's Revenge

Daniel tried to speak –
but he couldn't.
Omar had taken his voice
and he never gave it back.